# The Boosey & Hawkes
# Solo Piano Collection

## RACHMANINOFF

29 favourite themes arranged for
the intermediate pianist

Boosey & Hawkes Music Publishers Ltd
www.boosey.com

Published by Boosey & Hawkes Music Publishers Ltd
Aldwych House
71–91 Aldwych
London
WC2B 4HN

www.boosey.com

ISMN 979-0-060-12390-0
ISBN 978-0-85162-655-0

Third impression 2020

Printed by Halstan:
Halstan UK, 2-10 Plantation Road, Amersham, Bucks, HP6 6HJ. United Kingdom
Halstan DE, Weißliliengasse 4, 55116 Mainz. Germany

Music origination by Jon Bunker
Cover design by Fresh Lemon

# CONTENTS

# ARRANGER BIOGRAPHIES

HYWEL DAVIES

Hywel Davies is an award-winning composer, arranger and creative artist. His compositions have been performed by a wealth of ensembles including Kororo (Bournemouth Symphony Orchestra's new music ensemble, with whom he has a long-standing association), and have been broadcast internationally by the BBC, CBC (Canada) and ABC (Australia). In 2003 he was the recipient of an Arts Council England International Fellowship. As an arranger, Davies has been published by Boosey & Hawkes, Durand-Salabert-Eschig, Chester Music, Novello, the Associated Board of the Royal Schools of Music and Music Sales. Recent projects for Boosey & Hawkes have included *Folk Roots for Flute* & *Folk Roots for Clarinet*, two volumes of pieces by Ástor Piazzolla (*El viaje* & *Vuelvo al sur*), and a volume of works by Rachmaninoff (*Play Rachmaninoff*); he has also compiled several anthologies of piano music including most recently *Solitude*, *Russian Masters* and *Best of British* from the Boosey & Hawkes Solo Piano Collection. Davies is in demand as a sonic and installation artist, and has received commissions from organisations including Arts Council England and the National Trust, often working as an Artist in Residence.

www.hyweldavies.co.uk


NICHOLAS HARE

Nicholas Hare was born in 1940 and was a chorister at St George's Chapel, Windsor, under Dr William Harris. In 1954 he won a music scholarship to Marlborough College, Wiltshire, where he studied piano, organ and violin, and in 1959 was awarded a scholarship to Corpus Christi College, Oxford where he studied with Dr Sydney Watson. For ten years Nicholas served as Assistant Director and then Director of Music at Cheltenham College Junior, where he gained experience working with choirs and orchestras. During this period he also directed Music Vera chamber choir in Cheltenham. In 1979 he joined the editorial department of Chester Music working on a variety of educational projects and classical publications, including the preparation of new material for many premieres. Since 1990 Nicholas has worked as a freelance editor and arranger for Boosey & Hawkes, Chester Music, Faber Music, Trinity College London, the Associated Board of the Royal Schools of Music and others.

www.haremusic.co.uk


CHRISTOPHER NORTON

Christopher Norton was born in New Zealand in 1953. After graduating he began his career as a teacher, pianist and composer, and began to develop an interest in popular music. Coming to the UK in 1977 on a university scholarship, he studied composition at York University with Wilfred Mellers and David Blake. Well established as a composer, producer, arranger and educationalist, Norton has written stage musicals, ballet scores, piano music, popular songs and orchestral music as well as jingles and signature tunes for TV and radio. He has lectured all over the world on aspects of his work and likes to integrate traditional teaching methods with aspects of modern technology. Chris is best known for his world-famous series *Microjazz* — easy graded pieces in modern styles such as blues, rock 'n' roll, reggae and jazz — and for his award-winning *Essential Guides to Pop Styles*, *Latin Styles* and *Jazz Styles*.

www.christophernorton.com


ALFRED RICHTER (1902–1976)

Born in Austria in 1902, Alfred Richter moved to America at the age of 7 and studied piano with Walter Golz. For a number of years he was a piano tutor and lecturer in music history at Columbia College in South Carolina. He married former student and fellow composer and pianist Ada in 1932 and they made five international tours lecturing around the world on piano instruction. He wrote a number of books including *Rachmaninoff for Everyone* and *Rimsky-Korsakoff for Everyone* for Boosey & Hawkes in the 1940's. He died in 1976.

# ALEKO
## XI – Intermezzo

SERGEI RACHMANINOFF
arranged by Hywel Davies

**Allegretto pastorale**

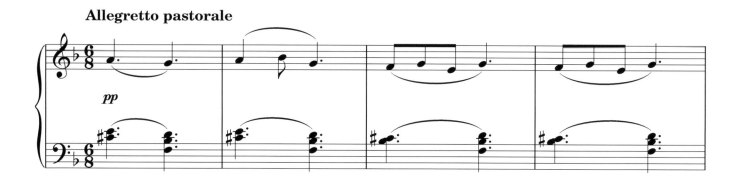

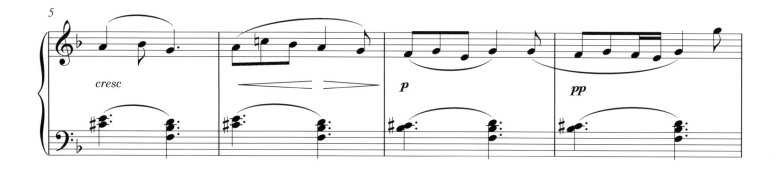

**L'istesso tempo**

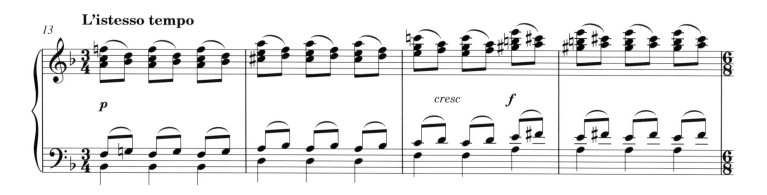

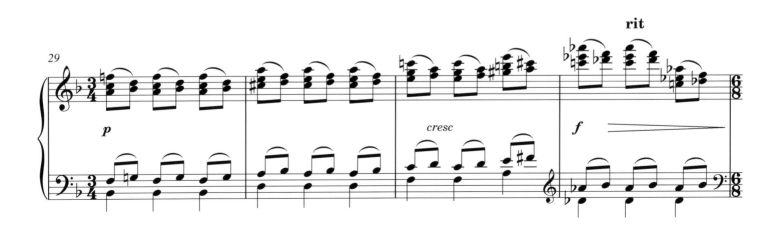

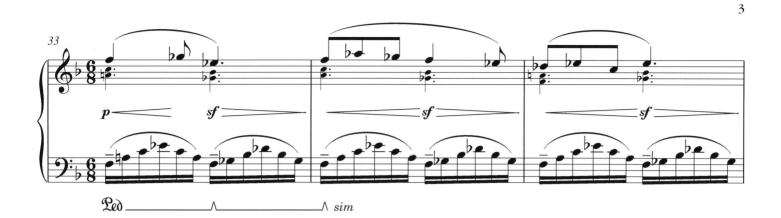

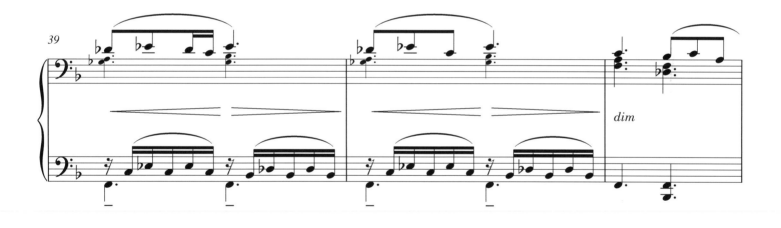

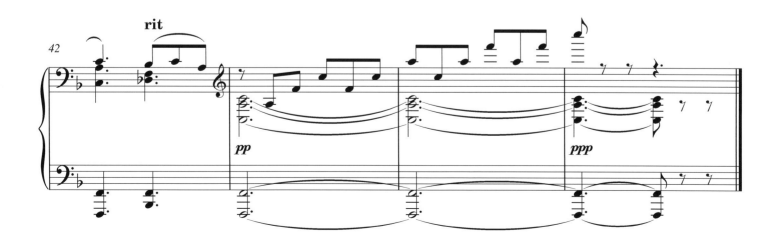

# ALEKO
## V – Women's Dance

SERGEI RACHMANINOFF
arranged by Hywel Davies

**Tempi di valse**

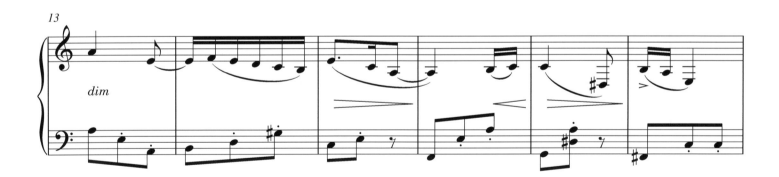

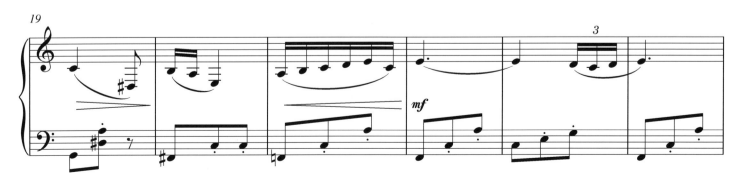

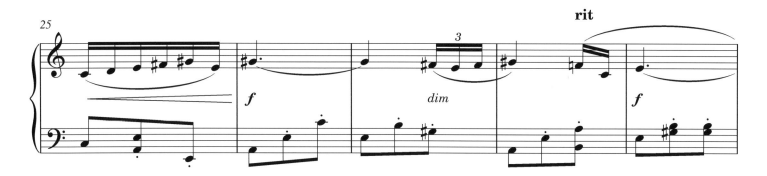

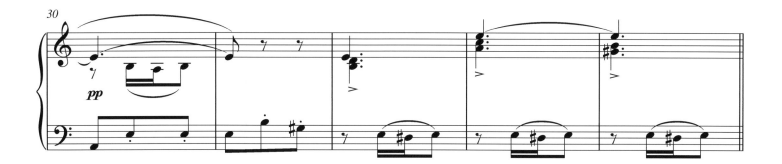

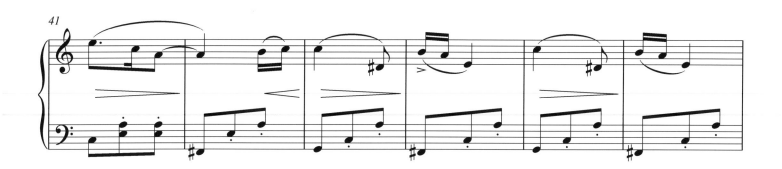

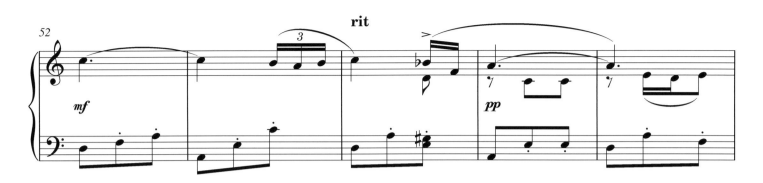

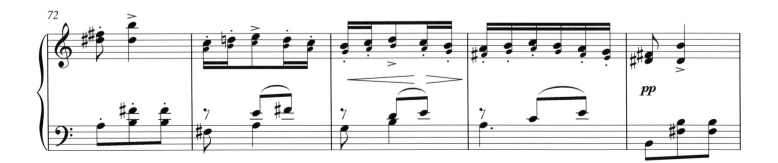

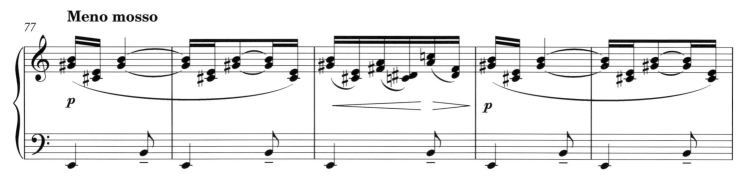

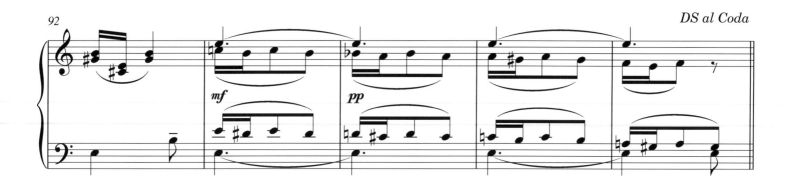

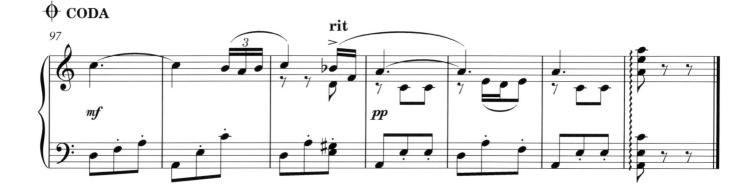

# ALEKO
## XII – Young gypsy's romance

SERGEI RACHMANINOFF
arranged by Hywel Davies

**un poco più mosso**

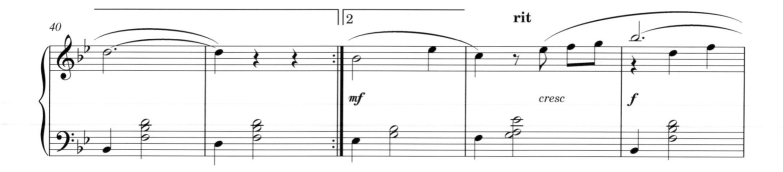

# ALL NIGHT VIGIL (VESPERS) Op 37
## O gentle light (Gladsome radiance)

SERGEI RACHMANINOFF
arranged by Hywel Davies

**Tempo Primo**

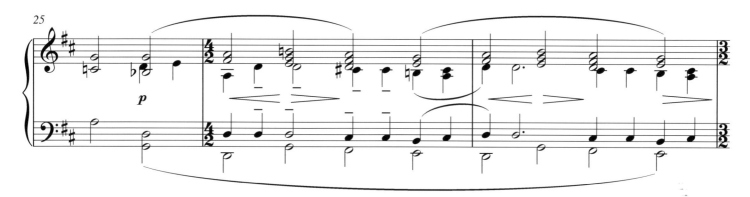

ritardano

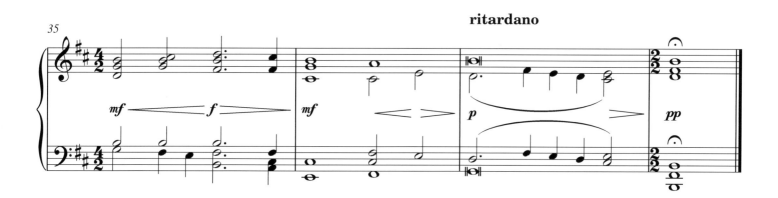

# FOURTEEN SONGS Op 34
## XIV - Vocalise

SERGEI RACHMANINOFF
arranged by Nicholas Hare

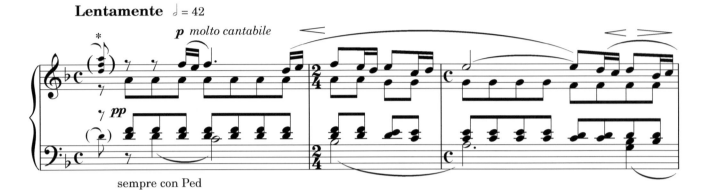

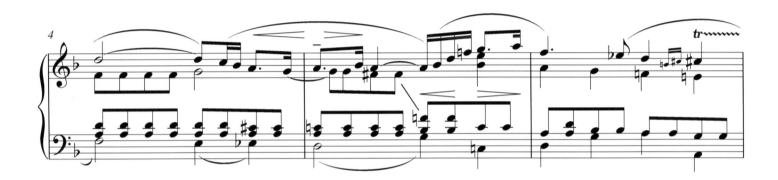

\* Small notes 2nd time only

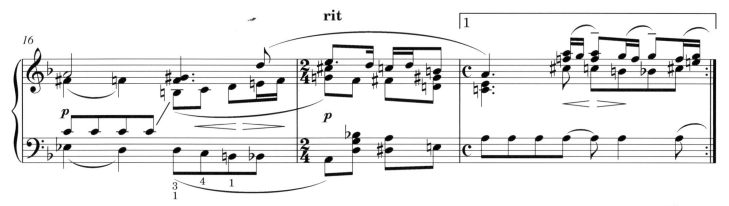

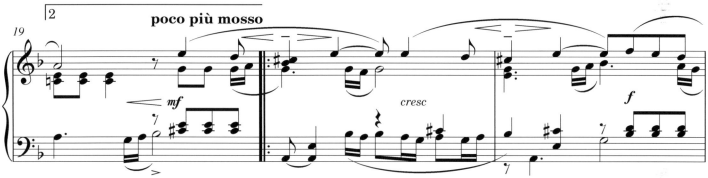

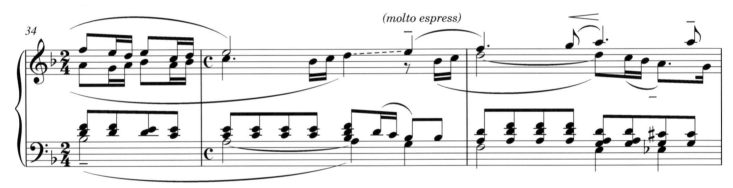

# MORCEAUX DE FANTAISIE Op 3
## I – Elégie

SERGEI RACHMANINOFF
arranged by Hywel Davies

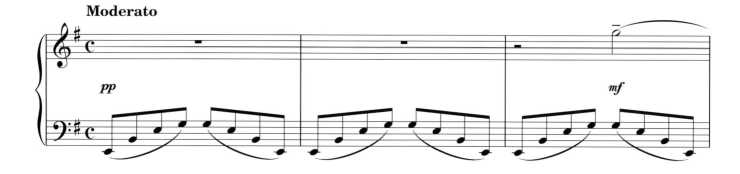

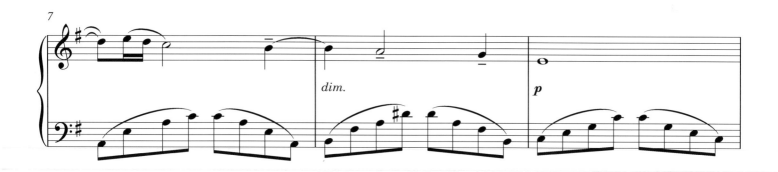

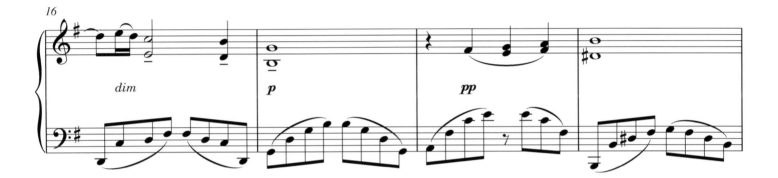

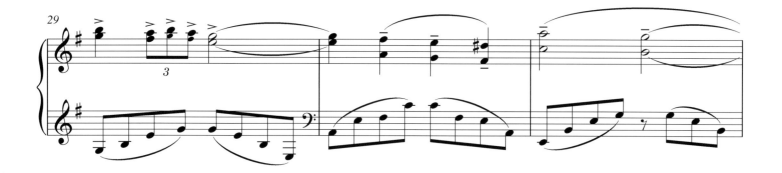

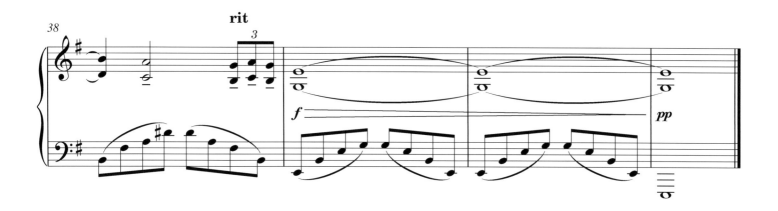

# MORCEAUX DE FANTAISIE Op 3
## II – Prelude *

SERGEI RACHMANINOFF
arranged by Nicholas Hare

* 'Prelude in C♯ minor' *(arranged in C minor)*

© Copyright 1893 by Hawkes & Son (London) Ltd.
This arrangement © Copyright 1993 by Boosey & Hawkes Music Publishers Ltd

agitato

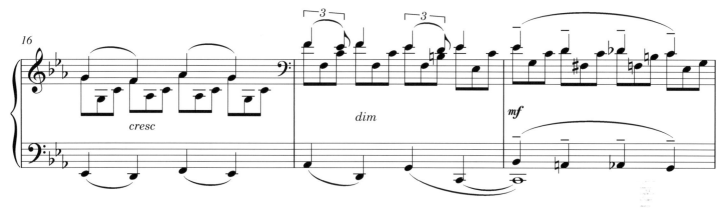

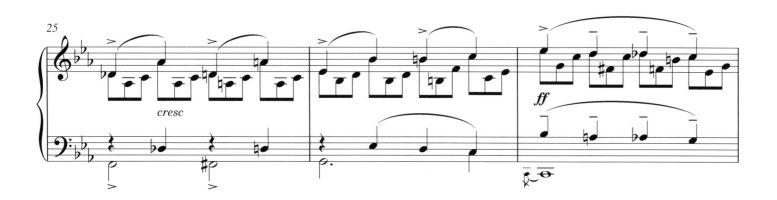

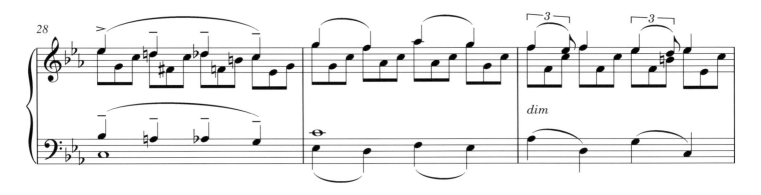

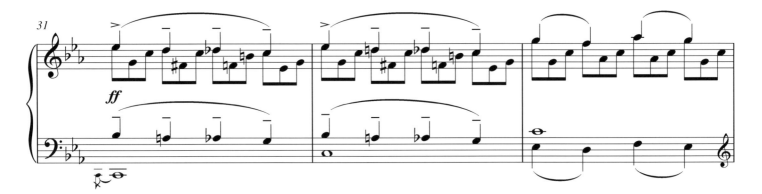

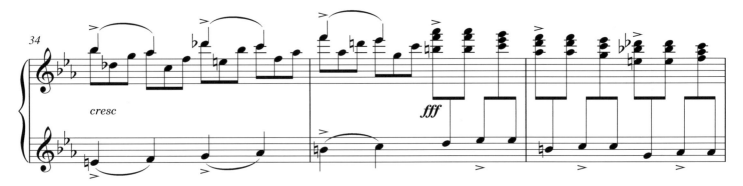

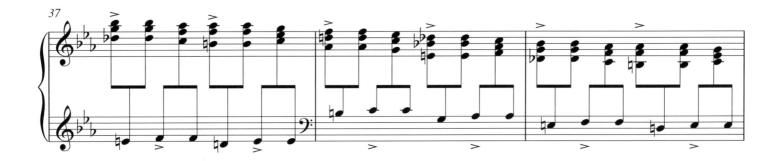

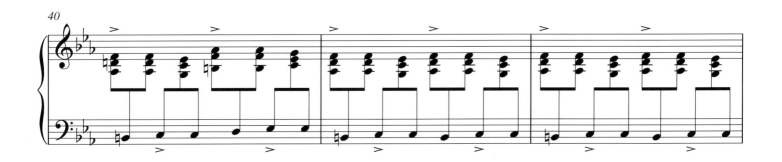

**Tempo primo**

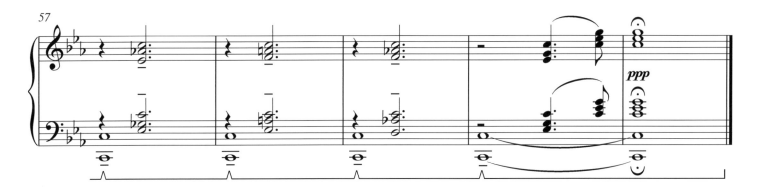

# MORCEAUX DE FANTAISIE Op 3
## V – Serenade

SERGEI RACHMANINOFF
arranged by Alfred Richter

**Sostenuto**

**Tempo di valse**

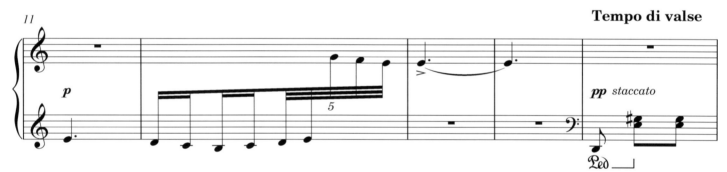

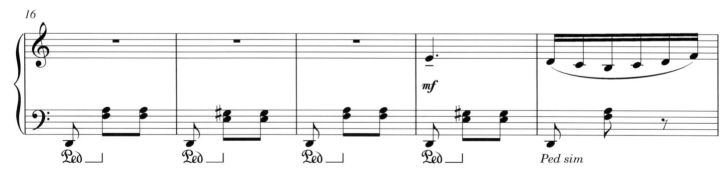

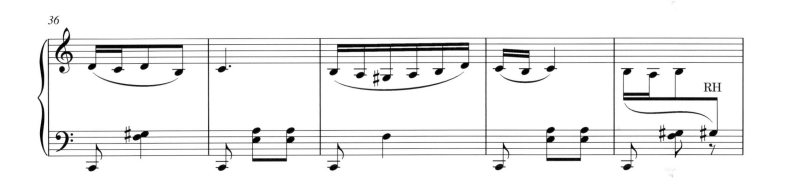

rit      a tempo

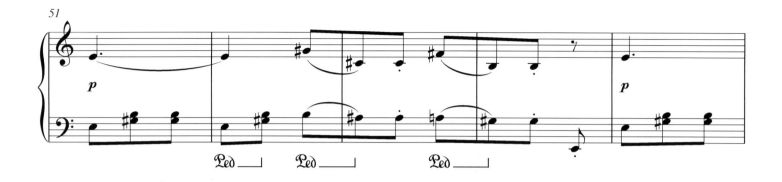

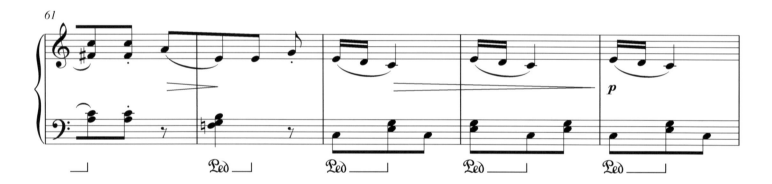

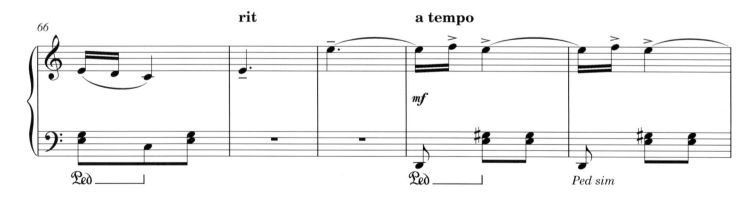

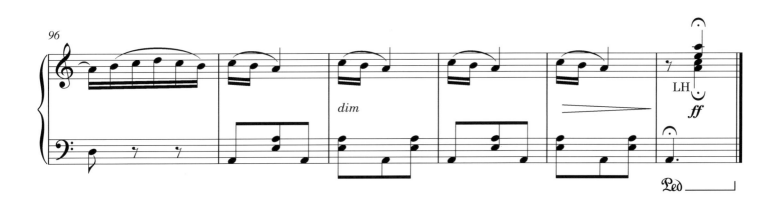

# MORCEAUX DE SALON Op 10
## VI – Romance

SERGEI RACHMANINOFF
arranged by Hywel Davies

**Andante doloroso**

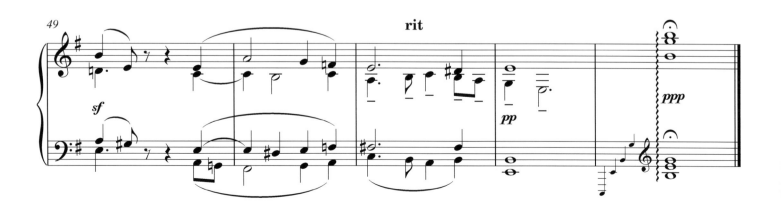

# PIANO CONCERTO No 3, Op 30
## Theme from first movement

SERGEI RACHMANINOFF
arranged by Nicholas Hare

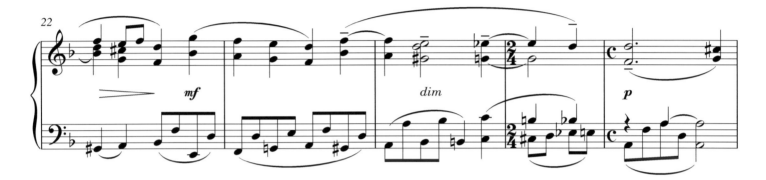

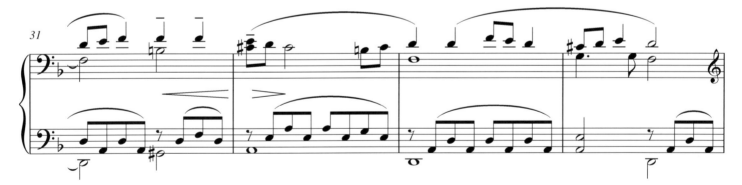

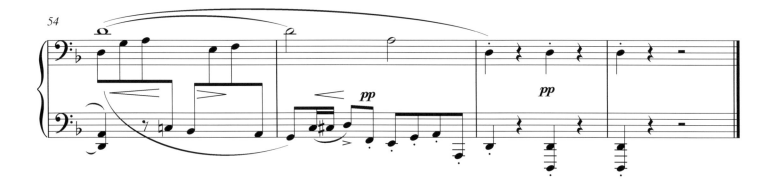

# PIANO CONCERTO No 2, Op 18
## Theme from first movement

SERGEI RACHMANINOFF
arranged by Christopher Norton

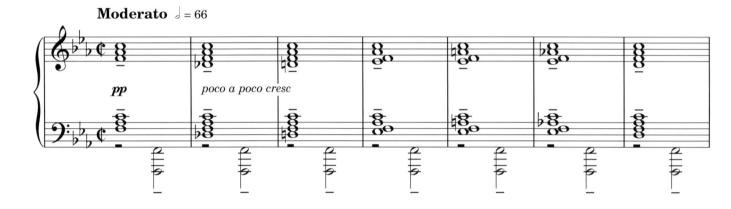

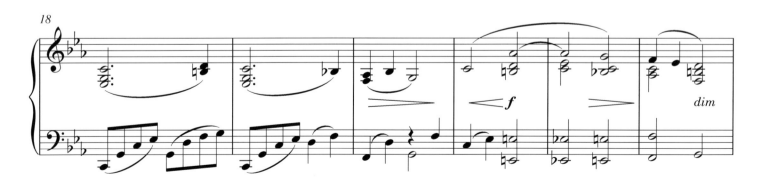

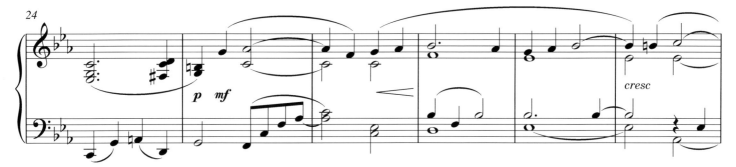

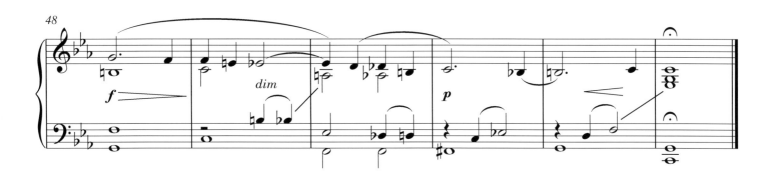

# PIANO CONCERTO No 2, Op 18
## Theme from second movement

SERGEI RACHMANINOFF
arranged by Hywel Davies

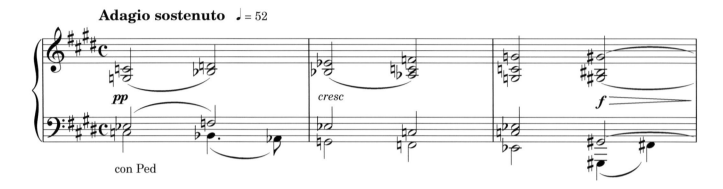

un poco più animato

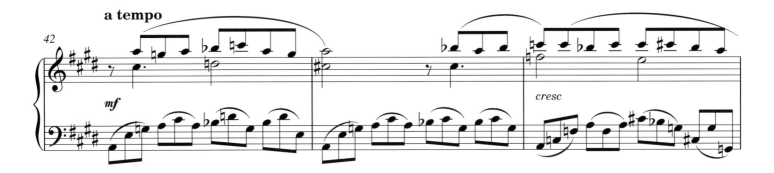

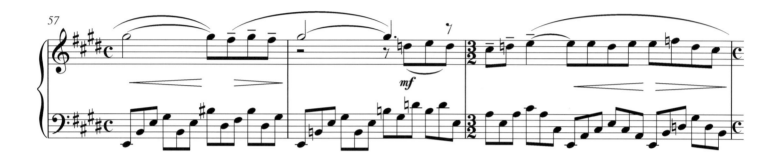

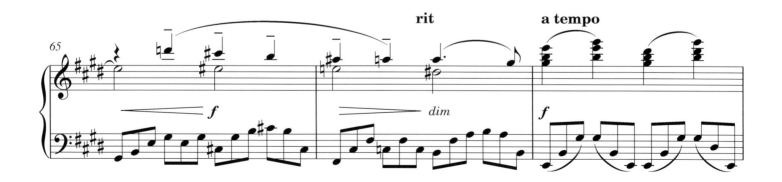

# PIANO CONCERTO No 2, Op 18
## Theme from third movement

SERGEI RACHMANINOFF
arranged by Christopher Norton

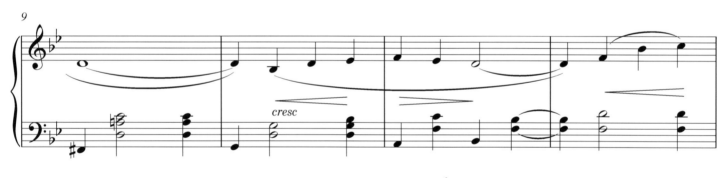

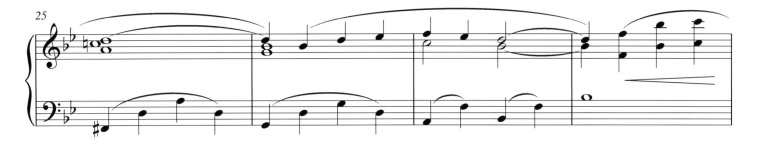

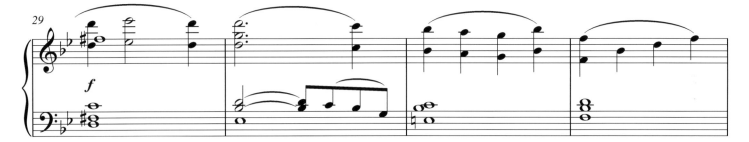

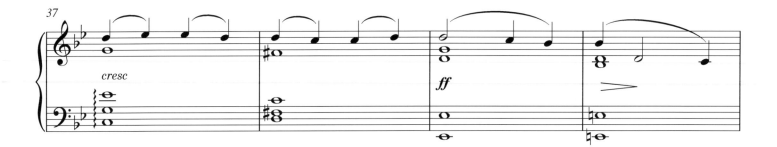

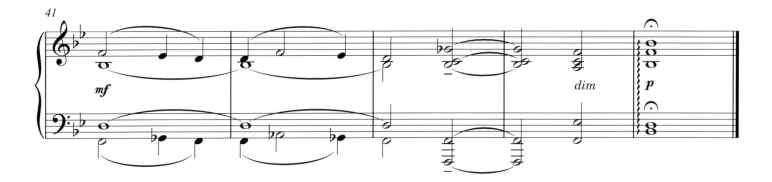

# PIANO CONCERTO No 3, Op 30
## Theme from second movement (Intermezzo)

SERGEI RACHMANINOFF
arranged by Hywel Davies

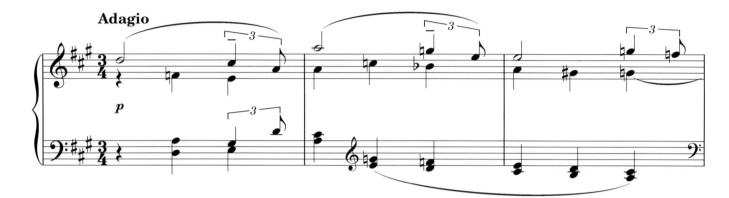

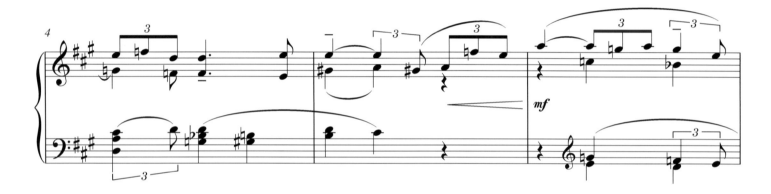

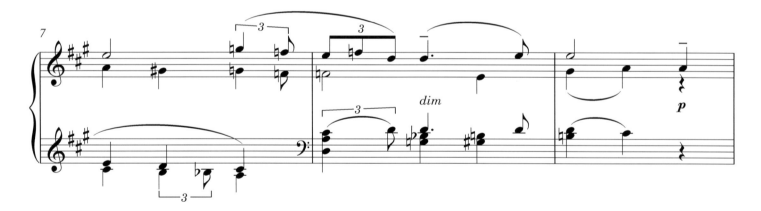

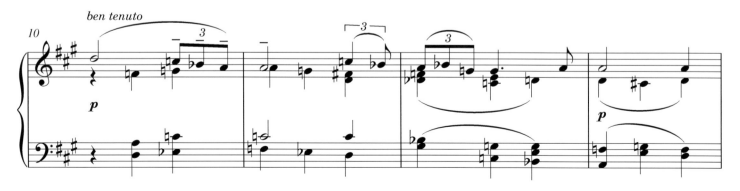

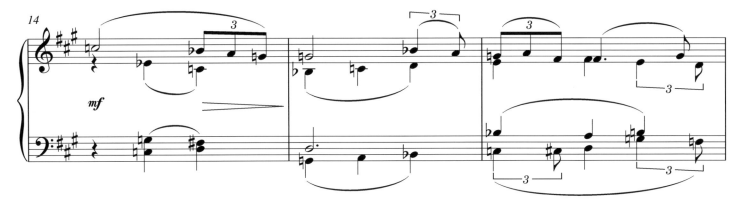

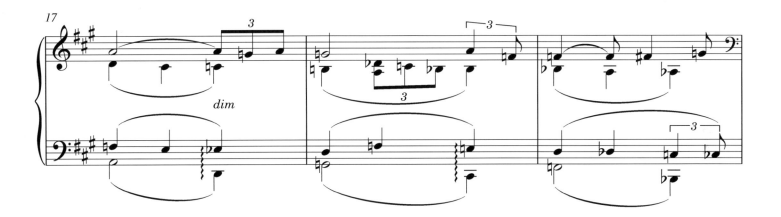

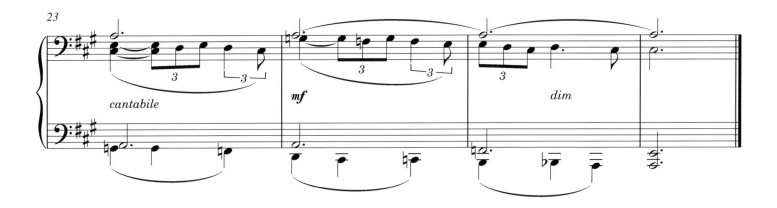

# PRELUDES Op 23, No 5

SERGEI RACHMANINOFF
arranged by Alfred Richter

**a little slower**

**Tempo I**

# PRELUDES Op 23, No 10

SERGEI RACHMANINOFF
arranged by Nicholas Hare

**accel poco a poco**

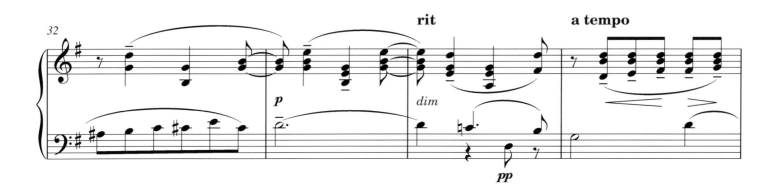

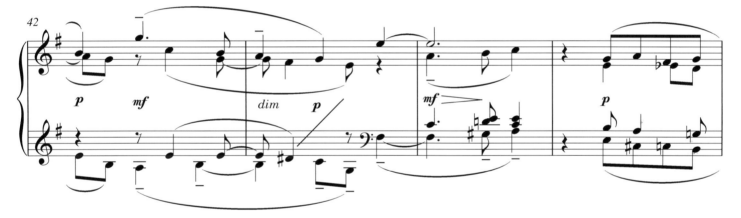

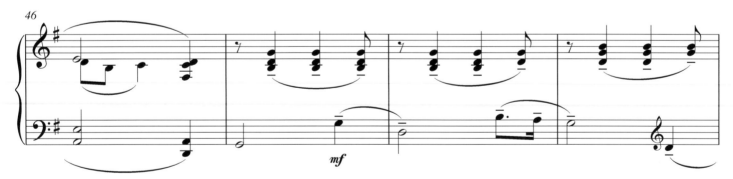

# RHAPSODY ON A THEME OF PAGANINI, Op 43
## Variation 18

SERGEI RACHMANINOFF
arranged by Hywel Davies

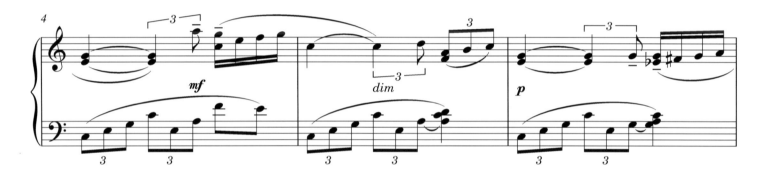

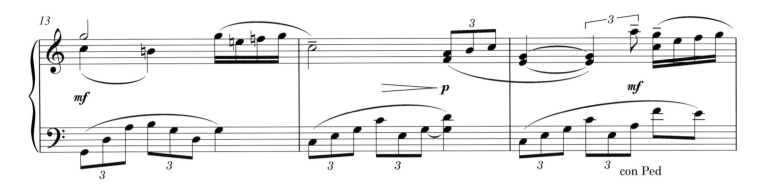

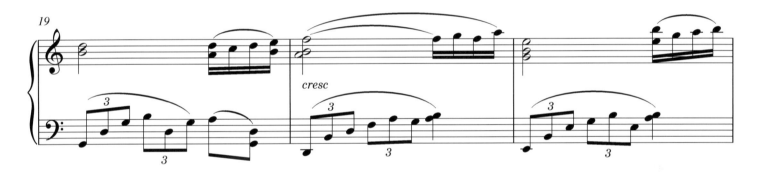

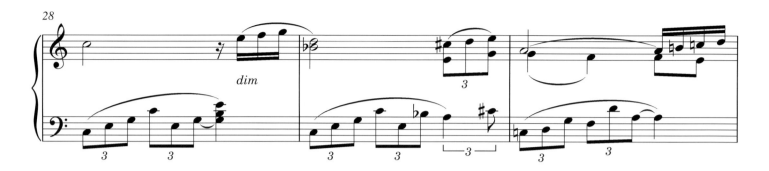

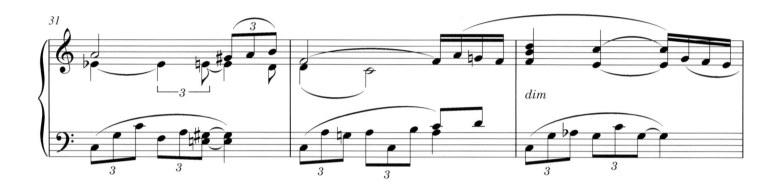

# THE LITURGY OF ST JOHN CHRYSOSTOM, Op 31
## XII – We praise thee (Tebe poem)

SERGEI RACHMANINOFF
arranged by Hywel Davies

# SIX MOMENTS MUSICEAUX, Op 16
## III – Andante cantabile

SERGEI RACHMANINOFF
arranged by Hywel Davies

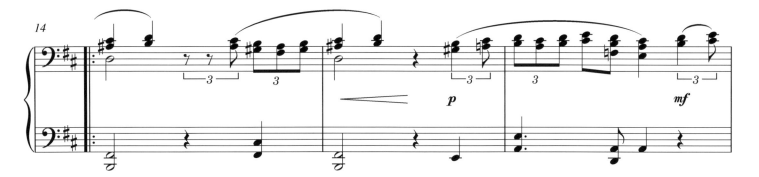

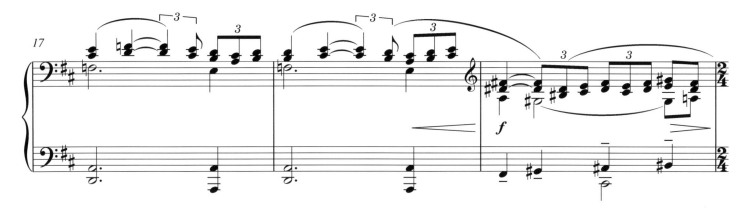

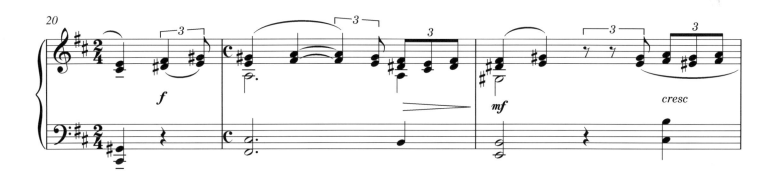

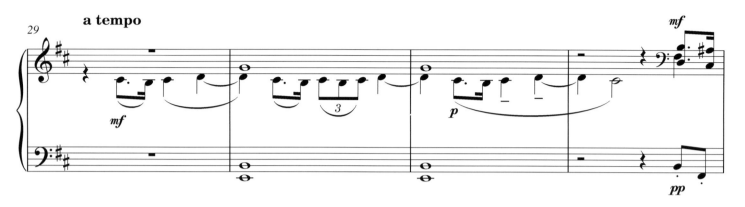

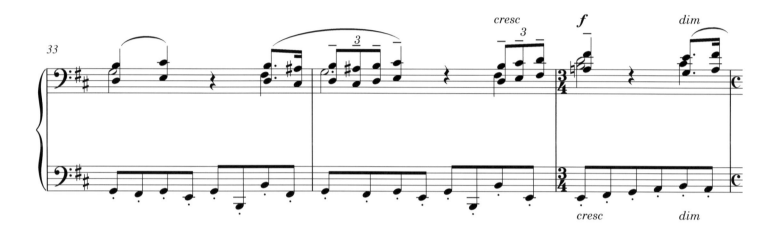

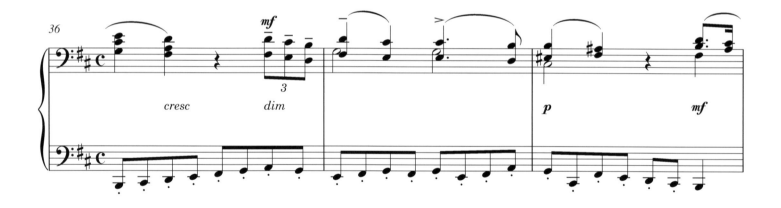

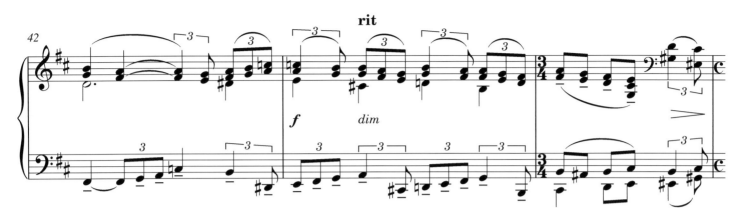

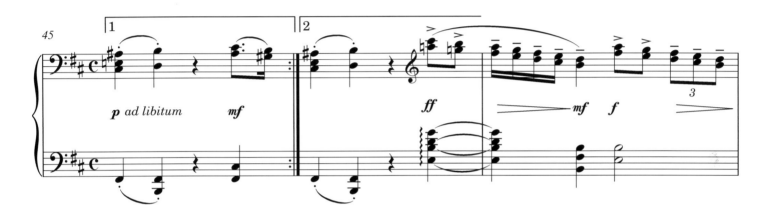

# SUITE No 2 FOR TWO PIANOS, Op 17
## II – Romance

SERGEI RACHMANINOFF
arranged by Alfred Richter

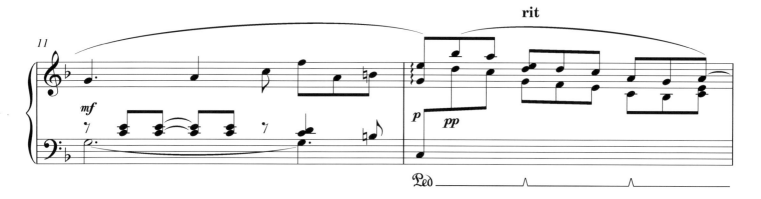

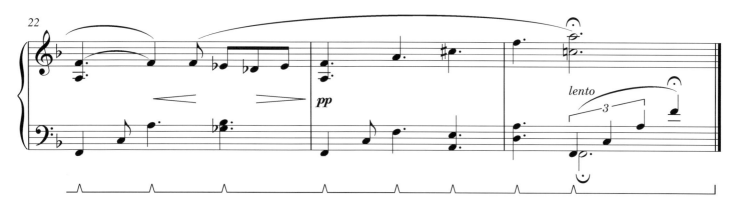

# SYMPHONIC DANCES, Op 45
## I – Non allegro

SERGEI RACHMANINOFF
arranged by Hywel Davies

63

# SYMPHONY No 2, Op 27
## Theme from second movement

SERGEI RACHMANINOFF
arranged by Nicholas Hare

**Allegro molto** ♩ = 126

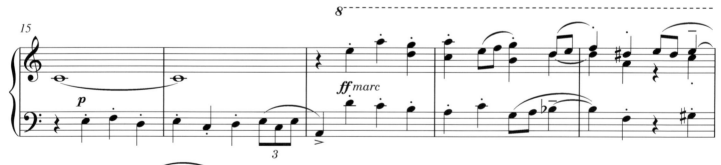

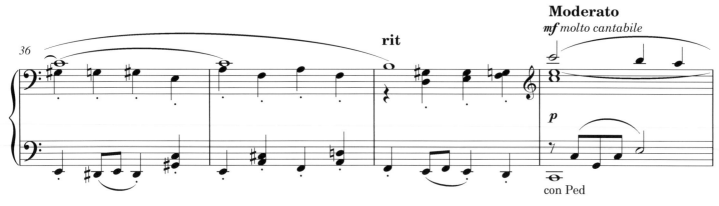

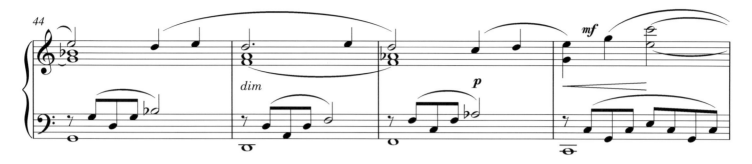

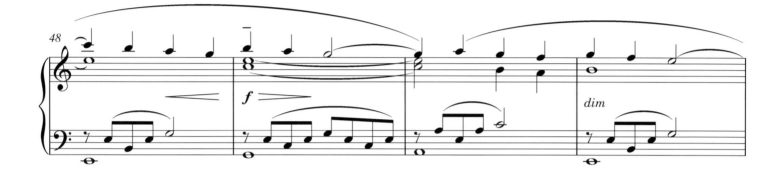

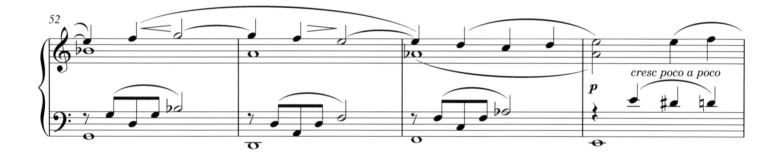

**Tempo I (subito)**

*DS al Coda*

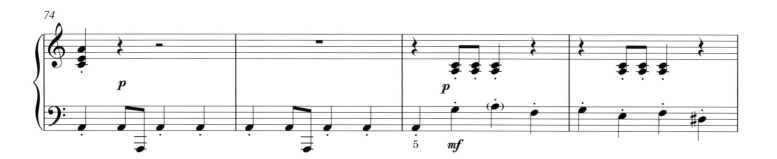

# SYMPHONY No 2, Op 27
## Theme from third movement

SERGEI RACHMANINOFF
arranged by Christopher Norton

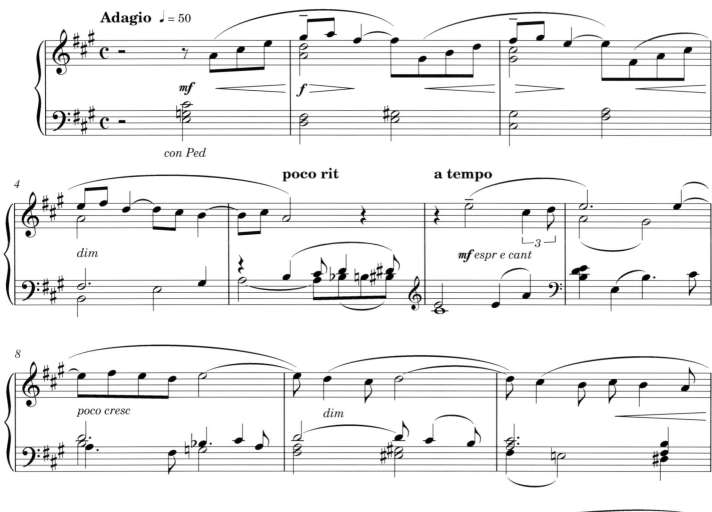

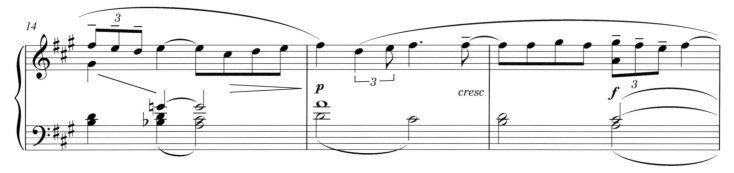

cx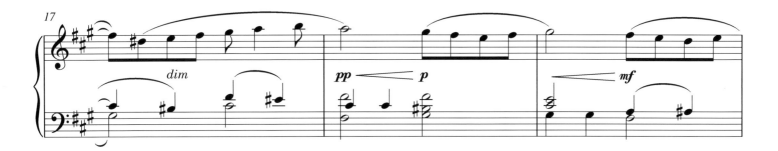

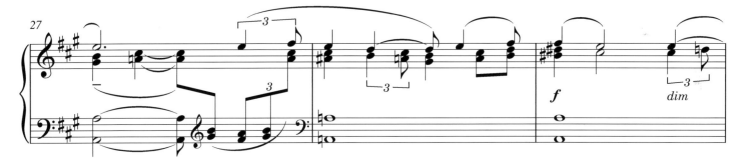

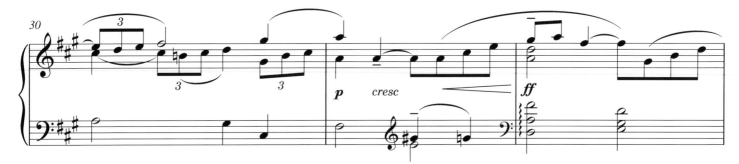

# SYMPHONY No 3, Op 44
## Theme from second movement

SERGEI RACHMANINOFF
arranged by Hywel Davies

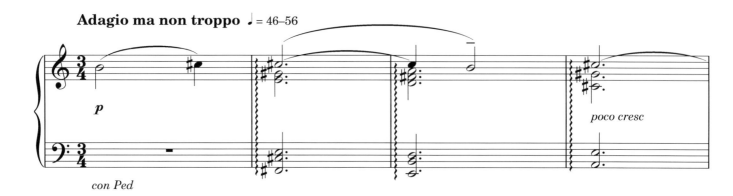

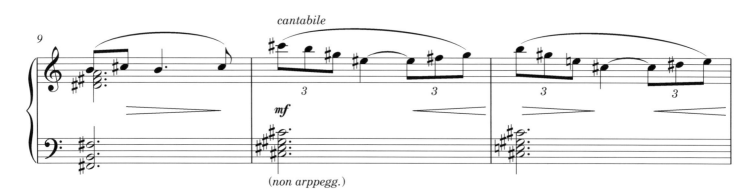

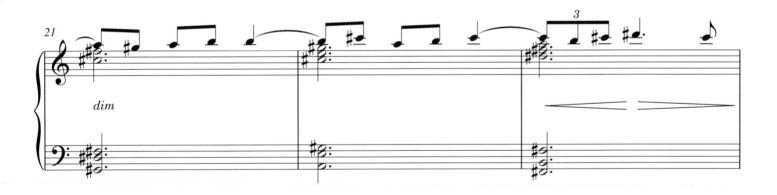

# SYMPHONY No 3, Op 44
## Theme from first movement

SERGEI RACHMANINOFF
arranged by Hywel Davies

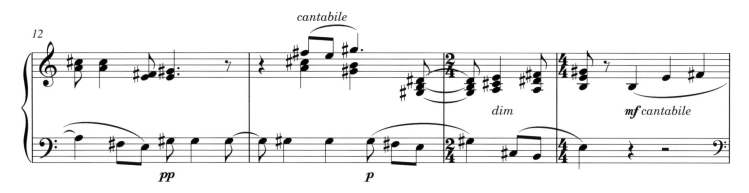

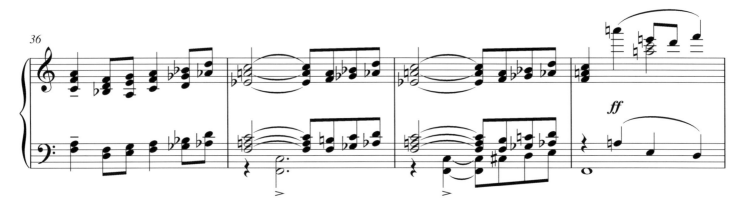

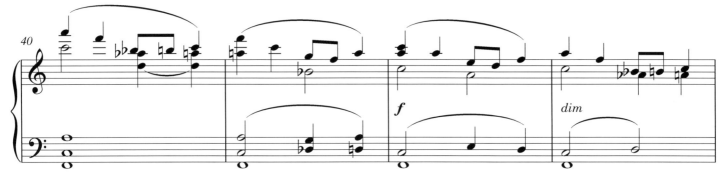

# TWELVE SONGS, Op 14

## IX – As fair as day in blaze of noon

SERGEI RACHMANINOFF
arranged by Hywel Davies

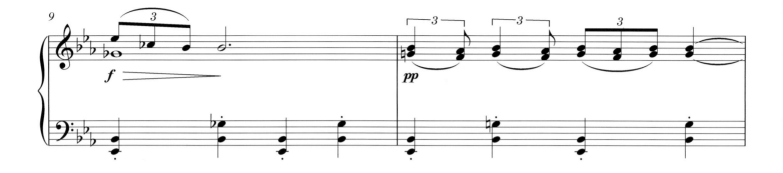

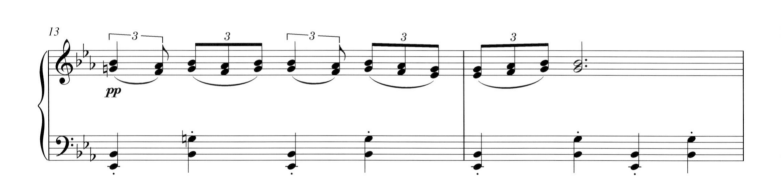

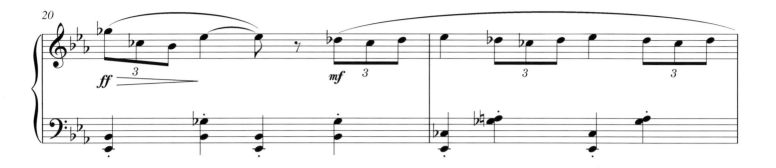

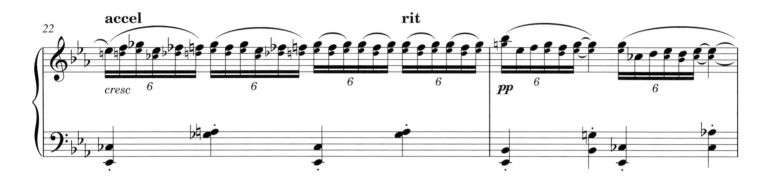

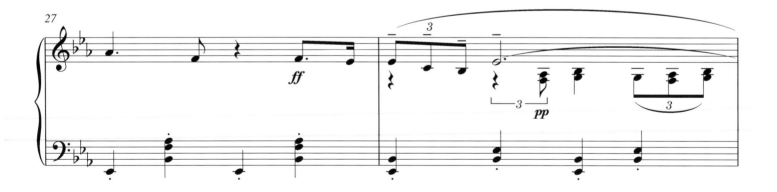

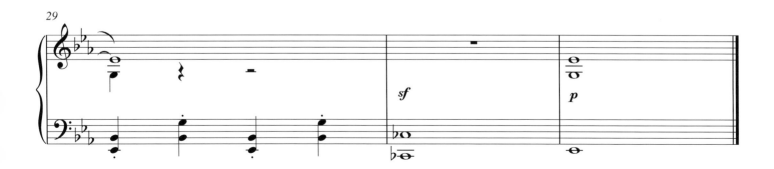

# TWELVE SONGS, Op 21
## V – Lilacs

SERGEI RACHMANINOFF
arranged by Hywel Davies

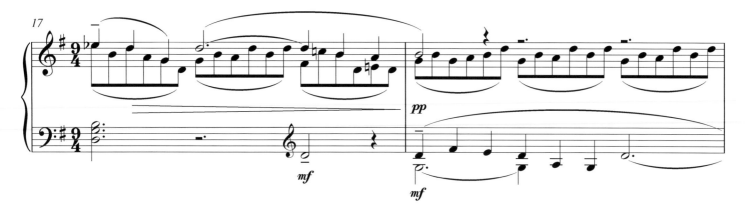

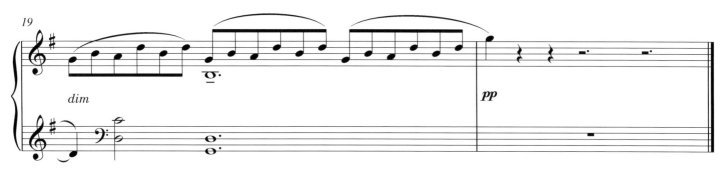

# VARIATIONS ON A THEME OF CORELLI
## Theme and variations (3, 12, 14 & 15)

SERGEI RACHMANINOFF
arranged by Hywel Davies

THEME

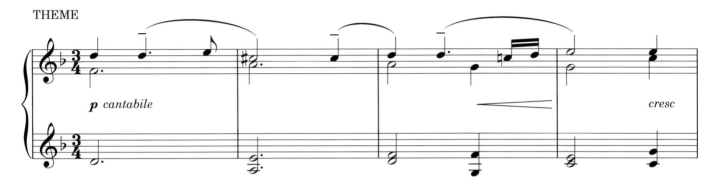

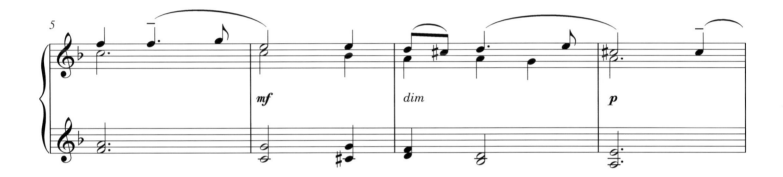

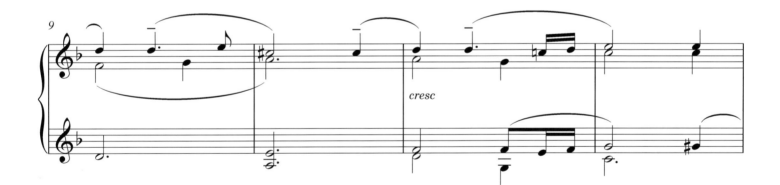

VARIATION III

**Tempo di Menuetto**

82

VARIATION XII

**L'istesso tempo**

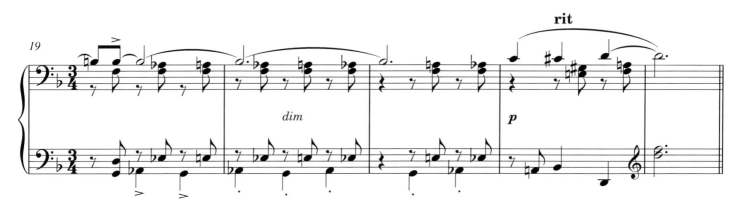

VARIATION XIV

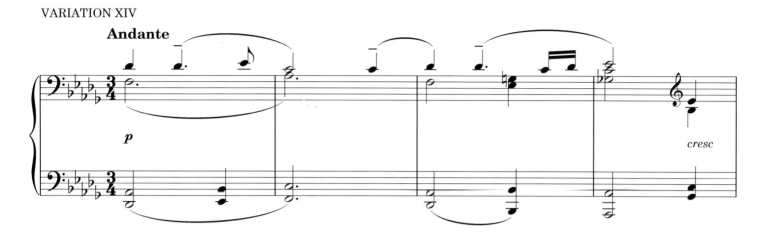

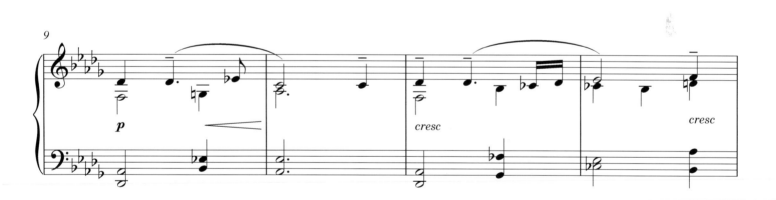

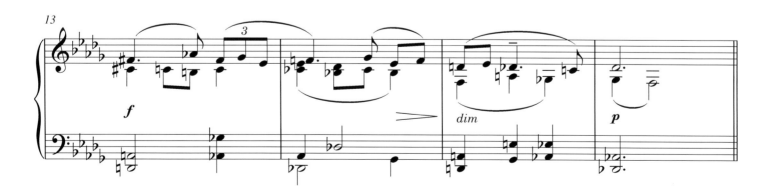

VARIATION XV

**L'istesso tempo [Andante come prima]**

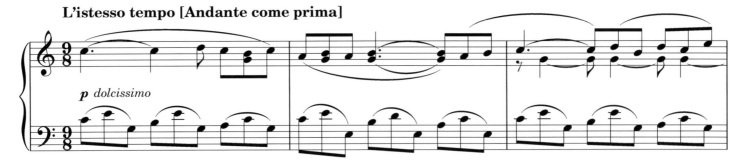

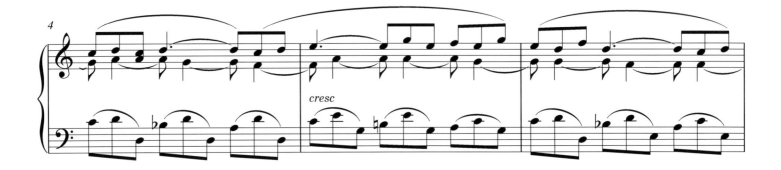

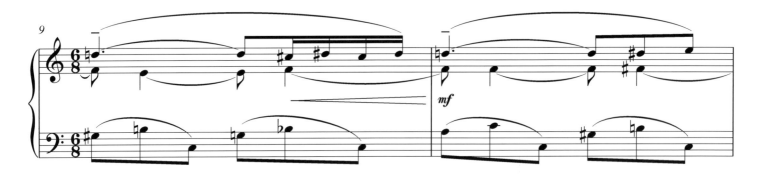

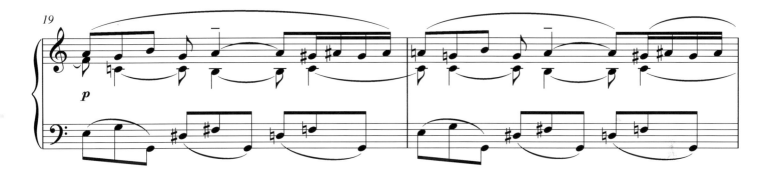

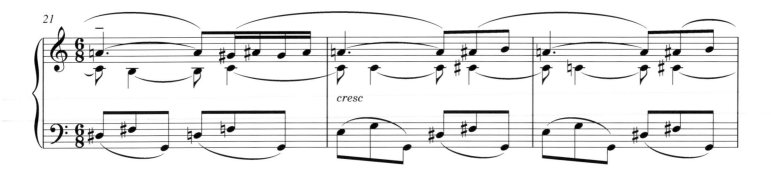

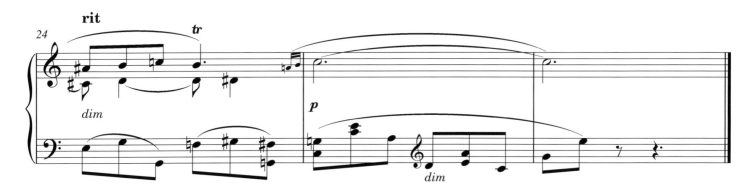

# TWO PIECES, Op 2
## II – Danse orientale

SERGEI RACHMANINOFF
arranged by Hywel Davies

**Andante cantabile**

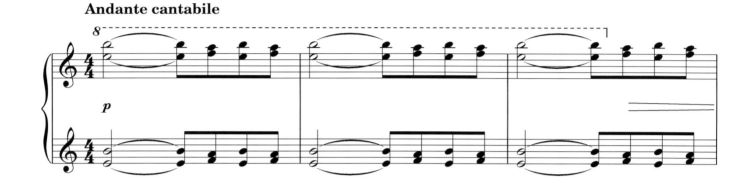

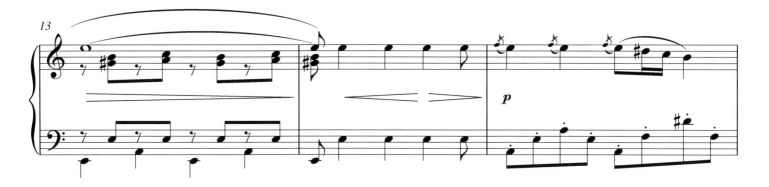

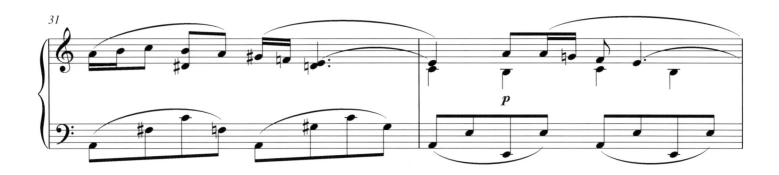

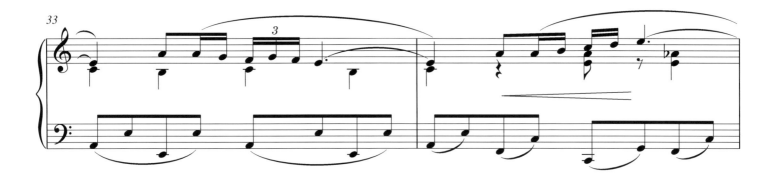

# Twentieth-Century Works for Piano

Bartók

*For Children* (volumes 1 & 2)
A new edition of Bartók's classic piano pieces. Revised with new engraving
and editorial notes by the composer's son, Peter Bartók

*Mikrokosmos* (volumes 1–6)
The definitive edition of the piano teaching classic. Includes an introduction by
Peter Bartók

Kabalevsky

*Easy Piano Compositions*
Contains *Four Little Pieces* op 14, *Twenty-four Little Pieces* op 39 and
*Four Rondos* op 60

Maxwell Davies

*Stevie's Ferry to Hoy*
Three simple pieces – *Calm Water*, *Choppy Seas* and *Safe Landing* –
with all the drama of a short journey by sea

Prokofieff

*Musiques d'enfants*
A piano repertoire classic published in the Russian Piano Classics series.
With introductions and performance notes by Peter Donohoe

*Peter and the Wolf* (arranged by Carol Barratt)
Prokofieff's classic children's tale in a charming new picture book edition.
The piano music is faithfully arranged by Carol Barratt and the story is retold
through verse with stunning full colour illustrations throughout

Rachmaninoff

*Play Rachmaninoff*
Nine of Rachmaninoff's greatest themes arranged for the intermediate
standard pianist. Includes Piano Concerto no 3 (theme from *Shine*),
Symphony no 2 (theme from movement 3), *Vocalise* and more

various

*20th-Century Easy Piano Collection*
A superb collection of music from some of the most important composers
of the last century. Includes pieces by 20th-century masters as well as less
familiar names and young composers of the current generation

*20th-Century Classics* (volumes 1 & 2)
Well known themes from 20th-century classics arranged for solo piano.
Includes Britten's *A Young Person's Guide to the Orchestra* and Copland's
*Hoe Down*. Also available arranged for piano duet

BOOSEY & HAWKES

Boosey & Hawkes Music Publishers Ltd
www.boosey.com

Ad. 371